# ALPACA
## SAVES CHRISTMAS

Rosemary Billam

Pictures by Vanessa Julian-Ottie

COLLINS

For Charlie and Otis

William Collins Sons & Co Ltd
London · Glasgow · Sydney · Auckland
Toronto · Johannesburg

First published 1990
© text Rosemary Billam 1990
© illustrations Vanessa Julian-Ottie 1990

ISBN 0 00 191398-0

A CIP catalogue record for this book is available
from the British Library

Printed and bound in Portugal by Resopal
This book has been set in Baskerville (Educational)

It was Christmas Eve. Ellen and Robert gazed at their Christmas tree sparkling in the firelight.

"Father Christmas is coming tonight," Ellen told Robert for the hundredth time.

Alpaca Rabbit looked up at the
fairy on top of the tree.

"Lucky thing," he thought.
"She'll see Father Christmas
when he comes."

Robert put some biscuits on a plate in case Father
Christmas was hungry, and Ellen poured out a glass
of milk and left it on the mantelpiece in case he was
thirsty as well.

Then they all sang Christmas carols round the tree until Daddy said it was time Alpaca went to bed.

Ellen sat Alpaca on her pillow while she had her bath. Alpaca could hear her singing in the bathroom. He felt warm and happy.

At bedtime the children hung their stockings at the end of their beds.

Ellen had made a small stocking especially for Alpaca. What a lovely surprise!

"I'm not going to sleep till Christmas comes," said Robert.

"Father Christmas won't come until you are fast asleep," said Mummy.

"Look out of the window and see if he's coming now," said Robert. But there was only a group of carol singers under the street lamp.

Ellen was tired, but
    sleep wouldn't come.

Alpaca couldn't settle either

. . . and Robert was wide awake. He stared at his
empty stocking. Suddenly he heard a noise outside.

"Sleigh bells," he said. He tiptoed over to the window and looked out.

"It's only a car," said Ellen.

The front door bell rang and there were voices and laughter in the hall. Robert scurried onto the landing and peered through the banisters.

He heard Mummy and Daddy coming upstairs, ran back to bed and pretended to be asleep when they peeped into the room. Only Alpaca had his eyes open. Robert kept absolutely still till he was sure that Mummy and Daddy were in bed. He had decided that the best way to see Father Christmas was to go downstairs and wait by the chimney.

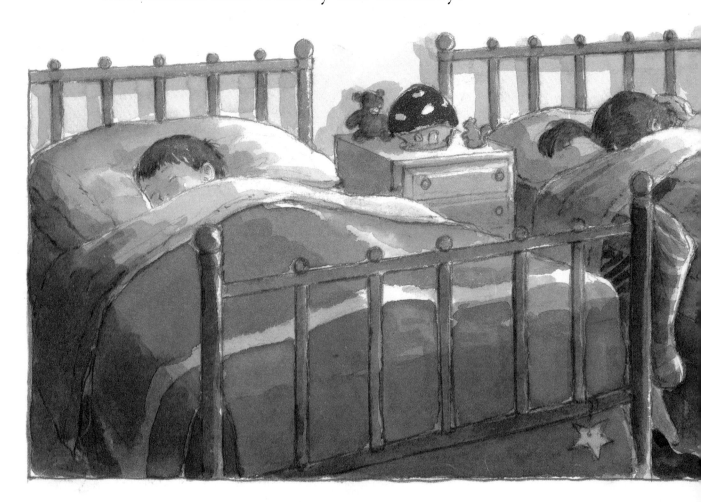

"Come on, Alpaca," he said. "We're going downstairs."

"I'd much rather stay in bed," thought Alpaca.

The house was very quiet and the stairs creaked.
The only light came from the street lamp outside.
Alpaca clung onto Robert as they crept downstairs.

Robert opened the door to the sitting room with a little click. The curtains were drawn, and it was very dark. He could just make out the shape of the tree with shadows all round it. He bent down to switch on the Christmas tree lights, and dropped Alpaca among the presents.

Just then, Robert heard footsteps in the hall
and he quickly hid behind the curtain. He held
his breath, but it was only Ellen.

"What are you doing down here?" she whispered,
taking his arm. "It's very late. Let's go back to bed.
We must be asleep before Father Christmas
comes."

They tiptoed upstairs, forgetting to switch off the lights on the Christmas tree.

"What about me?" thought Alpaca.

After a while he sat up and couldn't believe his eyes. He blinked and looked again.

There was Father Christmas with his sack. He stopped still, turned round and looked straight at Alpaca. Then he smiled a great big beaming smile.

"Well, well," he said. "I didn't expect to see you. Why aren't you tucked up in bed?"

Father Christmas put his sack on the floor and sat down in the armchair. He helped himself to the milk and biscuits.

"Very good," he said. He yawned, leaned back in the chair and nodded off to sleep.

"Oh dear," thought Alpaca. "What about all the other boys and girls who are waiting for him?"

Alpaca sat and watched Father Christmas snoring gently in the armchair. The clock in the hall struck one. Alpaca tried to nudge him awake, but it didn't work, so he tugged at his beard.

Father Christmas woke with a start. He looked at the clock on the mantelpiece.

"Bless me," he said. "I must hurry." He took Alpaca upstairs and put him back in Ellen's bed.

Alpaca lay there and watched as Father
Christmas filled the stockings with little parcels.
Then Father Christmas kissed Alpaca goodnight.
It must have been a magic kiss because Alpaca
went straight to sleep and he didn't remember
another thing.

In the morning, Ellen and Robert woke up early.
   "He's been! He's been!" shouted Robert,
waking up Alpaca who was still sound asleep. In
Alpaca's own little stocking, Ellen found a hat and
scarf which fitted him perfectly. Mummy peeped
round the door.

"Happy Christmas, darlings," she said.

"Christmas came," said Robert.

"So I see," said Mummy. "Aren't you lucky? Father Christmas must have been very hungry because he ate all the biscuits, and drank all the milk."

"So he did," thought Alpaca. "And nobody knows
I was there too, and that I even pulled his beard!"